the stocking filler

For my father

the stocking filler

A MODERN FABLE FOR CHRISTMAS

Rohan Candappa

Illustrations by Jonathan Millward

EBURY PRESS
LONDON

First published in 1998

1 3 5 7 9 10 8 6 4 2

First published in the United Kingdom in 1998 by Ebury Press
Random House, 20 Vauxhall Bridge Road, London SW1V 2SA

Random House Australia (Pty) Limited
20 Alfred Street, Milsons Point, Sydney, New South Wales 2061, Australia

Random House New Zealand Limited
18 Poland Road, Glenfield, Auckland 10, New Zealand

Random House South Africa (Pty) Limited
Endulini, 5a Jubilee Road, Parktown 2193, South Africa

Random House UK Limited Reg. No. 954009

Papers used by Ebury Press are natural, recyclable products made
from wood grown in sustainable forests.

A CIP catalogue record for this book is available from the British Library.

ISBN 0 09 186799 1

Printed and bound in the UK.

Everything you are about to read is completely true. Honest. Apart from the stuff I've made up.

It all started with Stanley.

Now Stanley worked with
Santa. He was Santa's
Stocking Filler.

This meant that when Santa did his rounds, Stanley would fill the stockings with presents while Santa checked off who got what from his list.

★ ★ ★

(Yes he has got a list, and he does check it twice to find out who's naughty or nice, and I don't know how to break this to you, but at the moment you're well ensconced on the naughty side.)

But Stanley did a lot more than just fill the stockings.

You see, it was actually Stanley who would go down the chimney, then let Santa in through the front door.

Girthically challenged would be a polite way of putting it.

Well, let's face it, Santa is not
the sveltest individual around.

And a chimney is a notoriously narrow neck of the woods.

In fact, the well known comedy song 'When Santa Got Stuck In The Chimney' was based on a series of events that took place in the early 1950s just north of Stavanger in Norway that so very nearly ended in tragedy. But I digress.

★ ★ ★ ★ ★

Santa's state of health was
beginning to worry Stanley.

You see, every year Santa's sack was getting heavier and heavier. That's because every year kids were getting more and more presents. And every year Santa was finding it harder to lift his sack.

So Stanley did what he always did when he was unsure what to do.

No, he didn't go and get a kebab.

He went to his bookshelf. You see, Stanley loved books. He thought that in books he could find out anything he wanted to know.

★✦★
★✦★

So Stanley got out his big book on family health and had a bit of a peruse. And that's when he became really worried.

Santa was ironing his spare hood in the kitchen when Stanley burst in.

'Boss,' blurted out Stanley 'I think we should go and see the doctor because I'm worried you might have a heart attack and die.' Tact was not one of Stanley's strong points.

'Subtle, Stanley. Very subtle,' said Santa, and went on ironing.

'Pleeeeeaaaassseeee!' countered Stanley, in as coherent an argument as he could muster.

'Oh , okay' said Santa ' there's nothing decent on the telly anyway.There never is at Christmas.'

The doctor asked about Santa's lifestyle. Which was 364 days a year of general sitting about. And one night of mad rushing round with lots of heavy lifting.

The doctor asked about Santa's diet. Which was frozen mince pies washed down with sherry. (That's what people leave out for him.)

And then she listened to Santa's heart.

'Aaah,' said the doctor.

'Oh,' said Stanley.

‘He's got a heart murmur,’
said the doctor.

‘What's a heart murmur?’
said Stanley.

The doctor put the earpieces of her stethoscope to Stanley's ears and let him listen.

At first Stanley heard nothing. He was just about to give up when he detected a very faint, but insistent voice.

'I'm okay. It's nothing. Don't worry about me. I'm okay. It's nothing. Don't worry about me,' mumbled the voice.

Back at Santa's semi the mood was glum. Stanley looked at Santa and Santa looked at Stanley.

'She says you've got to take it easier,' said Stanley.

'So how am I going to do that?' asked Santa.

★★★

Stanley racked his brain. It didn't take long. He didn't have a very big brain.

‘I know,’ he said, as inspiration seized him and he leapt up like Archimedes jumping out of the bath that time when he filled it with cold water by mistake.

'Why don't we have Christmas off. I mean no-one else has to work Christmas, why should we?'

★ ✦ ✦ ★

'You haven't really thought this through, have you Stanley?' said Santa.

'What do you mean?' said Stanley, a little crestfallen.

'Stanley, I'm Father Christmas, if I don't work Christmas then I'm just a postman in a dodgy red uniform with naff white furry bits. I have to work Christmas. It's what I do.'

'Oh,' said Stanley, by way of a countering argument.

'No,' said Santa 'the problem isn't what I do, it's how much.'

✦★✦✦

Stanley looked confused.
(It was a look he was good at.)

'What I mean is,' continued Santa, 'that my sack never used to be this heavy. I never used to have to give kids so many presents. So many things. Maybe that's the problem.'

Stanley looked even more confused. 'But surely having lots of presents is good,' he said.

★ ★ ★

'Yeah, that's what I always thought. But just lately I'm beginning to have my doubts. I mean sometimes kids get so much stuff, so many things, that I'm not sure any of it means anything to them,' said Santa.

‘So what do we do, Boss?’
asked Stanley.

‥★☆★‥

'We can't do anything Stanley. You see, it's not up to me. It's up to the people we work for.'

'But I work for you, Boss.'

'Yes you do Stanley. But we both work for Festivco. Festivco plc.'

'Festiv-who?' said Stanley.

At this point in the story a brief historical aside may prove illuminating.

You see, a few years back, there was a fashion for selling things off. It was called privatisation. And while more high-profile privatisations dominated the front pages, the sneakiest deal of all took place while no-one was looking.

Christmas was sold off. To the highest bidder.

And that's why Christmas is now, in fact, a wholly-owned subsidiary of Festivco plc.

Amongst the first actions the new owners of Christmas undertook was a round of deeply irrational 'rationalisation'.

To put it bluntly they downsized
the whole 'Santa's Little
Helpers Department'.

To put it even more bluntly,
they gave everyone the sack
apart from Stanley.

Which is how Stanley, by no means the smartest cookie in the jar, but by far the lowest paid, got to be promoted to the heady heights of Stocking Filler.

(Previously he'd just been the junior trainee under-assistant in the bauble storage department.)

But Stanley didn't know any of this. Which is why he repeated his question.

'Festiv-who?' he said.

Santa went over to his desk, and from a drawer crammed to overflowing with doubles from his beermat collection, he pulled out his contract.

★★★★★

'Festivco plc' he said, showing Stanley the headed piece of paper. Stanley studied the contract.

'I know,' said Stanley, 'I'll go and talk to them. Once they understand the situation I'm sure they'll help.'

✦★✹★

'Stanley,' said Santa 'I don't think it's that simple.'

⋆★⋆★⋆

But Stanley was already
halfway out of the door.
'I'll be back,' he said in his
best Arnold Schwarzenegger
voice.

Santa watched him go. Sighed.
Then got out his glockenspiel
and started to practise
Madonna songs. It was what
he always did when he was
worried.

Finding the headquarters of Festivco plc was easy. The building was massive.

✦ ★ ✦ ★ ✦

Stanley walked up to it through the car park, where there were spaces marked out for all the really important people.

'Of course!' he cried, as inspiration seized him and he leapt up, a leap that this time was more like Bob Stokoe leaping to his feet after the underdogs Sunderland won the 1973 Cup Final against the mighty Leeds United, 'I'll get in through the chimney!'

He stopped, sat down and pondered. While his reflection reflected. And that's when he saw the wisp of smoke wafting round the corner.

★☆★

Stanley followed the smoke around the corner. But, much to his surprise, it wasn't a chimney he found.

Instead it was a group of women, in skirts and blouses, arms tightly folded against the cold, all puffing away on cigarettes, huddled by a door.

A door that one of them was holding open.

Stanley sneaked in.

The inside of the building was very smart indeed. Everything was done out in taupe and puce – the corporate colours of Festivco plc.

But there was no-one to be seen. Anywhere.

Stanley wandered up and down corridors. He opened doors to offices. He took the lift to different floors.

He even checked out the
ladies' loos. (Just the same as
the men's except no urinals –
obvious really.)

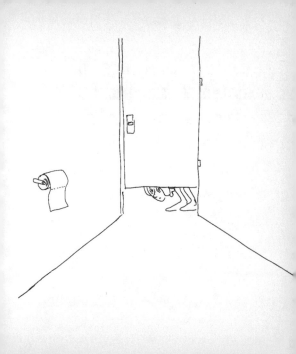

Eventually he found himself in
the basement walking down a
long taupe-and-puce corridor.

At the end of the corridor was a massive pair of doors over which hung a sign that proclaimed in big letters: 'Season's Greed Things from Festivco plc.'

Just as Stanley reached the doors they swung open and a hobbit pushed past him, explaining 'Sorry, I'm in the wrong story,' and scarpered down the corridor.

Stanley nipped through the doors before they swung shut again.

He found himself in an enormous conference hall. Hundreds of people sat in serried rows watching a presentation.

(No, I don't know what 'serried'
means either.)

A little man in a grey suit, sitting on the stage, was speaking. 'And now before we move on, here are three of the new products and services we are launching during the current Christmas offensive.'

'First there's "Snowflakes Direct" – why dream of a White Christmas, when all the snow you could ever wish for is only a phone call away?'

A picture filled the screen behind the man of children gleefully playing in a snow-covered garden, while the family next door watched enviously from their snow-free waste land.

✦ ★ ✦ ★ ✦

'Then there's "Rudolph-A-Pet" – soft felt strap-on antlers and battery-powered red noses that'll turn your much loved family pet into your very own Rudolph. Available in dog, cat and goldfish sizes.'

The picture changed to a red-nosed cat with antlers.

'And finally "Reindeer Steaks"
– at last a truly festive
alternative to the Christmas
turkey.'

The picture changed again to a small girl tucking into a great big steak. With relish. (Onion relish, I think.)

The audience clapped and
cheered each slide. Stanley
watched, fascinated but
appalled. Or appalled but
fascinated. (I'm not sure which.)

★⋆★⋆★

'But now let us focus on this year's key corporate message. Last year our slogan, "A guilty parent is a vulnerable consumer" helped us achieve record profits.'

By now the man was on his feet whipping the audience up into a frenzy.

'This year we want to smash all records, and we've refined our message down to a results-orientated, user-friendly, take no prisoners, call to arms!'

The lights in the hall dimmed. Wagner's 'Ride of the Valkyries' boomed from the speakers. The audience were on their feet, stomping and screaming their approval.

'This year's slogan is…'
shouted the little man,
' "The More Presents You Get,
The More People Love You." '

The words flashed up one by one on to the screen as he spoke. And the crowd went wild, punching the air triumphantly.

'Oh dear,' said Stanley. He made his way, quietly, out of the hall.

Stanley wandered about aimlessly. His plan of talking to the people who ran Festivco plc was beginning to look a little naive.

He found himself outside a kitchen and decided to make a coffee to steady his nerves. It was while he was hunting for a clean teaspoon that he spotted the Secret Memo.

✦✭✮✭✦

It was lying around next to the decaf and on the cover it said:

'Secret Memo –
Don't Leave Lying
Around Next to the
Decaf.'

The first page read,

'The more presents
people get, the more
profits Festivco plc
make.'

The second page read,

'Children are our primary
target because they are
pure consumers, untainted
by doubt. And children
are gullible.'

Now 'gullible' was a word
Stanley hadn't come across
before. So he pulled his trusty
dictionary from his satchel and
looked it up.

'Gullible: derives from gull or seagull – a very stupid and easily misled creature. For example, someone once told a gull that rubbish tastes nice and that's why rubbish dumps are always covered with scoffing gulls.'

✦✶✦

And then Stanley turned to the
last page of the Secret Memo.
It was headed

'The Santa Demise
     Scenario.
How to Maximise
     Income.'

'We realise that if current workload-increase projections are fulfilled in the forthcoming fiscal year then we will be faced with the very real prospect of a "death in service" type scenario in regards to employee K768/001 Mr S. J. Claus.

★ ★ ★

We believe that this
represents not a problem,
but a major marketing
opportunity. Mr Claus's
demise would provide a
unique window for
Festivco plc to
reinvigorate the whole
Santa franchise in much
the same way that the

✦ ★ ✦

Sales could be co-ordinated
through a network of
official Memorial Grottoes
that act both as local
centres of pilgrimage and
retail outlets. The first
year after Santa's demise
(Year D1 in all forthcoming
discussions) we see massive
marketing potential in the

death of Elvis did for
Elvis. We envisage the
launch of a whole new
range of memorial
products and re-issues of
back catalogue Santa
merchandise. Premium
prices could also be
obtained for genuine,
certified Santarabilia.

slogan – "Give More Presents, It's What He Would Have Wanted." In short, the U.D. (Ultimate Downsizing) of employee K768/001 need not signal the end of the Santa brand, but a whole new, vastly profitable, beginning.'

★★*

Stanley folded the memo up,
put it in his satchel and fled.

⋆★⋆★⋆

Back at the house Santa was
Hoovering the landing.

'So,' said Santa, 'what did they say?'

Stanley didn't reply. He didn't know where to begin. So he just handed over the memo.

Then he went and poured
Santa a large sherry.

Santa read the memo. Drank the proffered sherry. Read the memo again. And poured himself another sherry, while he pondered his own demise.

'I'm sorry, Boss,' said Stanley.

'Bastards,' said Santa.

'So what are we going to do?'
asked Stanley.

Santa downed the second sherry, poured himself a third and said, 'We're going to come up with a plan.'

There was a long pause while neither of them could come up with a plan.

There was a slightly shorter, but entirely separate pause, that followed the first pause, while both of them had stopped trying to come up with a plan, but were waiting expectantly for the other's solution.

The second pause ended too.
And Santa spoke.

'We could go on strike,' he
said.

‘Or we could run away,’ he continued.

'To Zanzibar,' chipped in Stanley, not wanting to be completely left out of the plan-making process.

There was a third, altogether different, pause. A pause of a slightly more chewy consistency.

★⋆★⋆

'But', said Santa, as he sat down forlornly in his favourite chair and emptied the last of the sherry into his glass, 'I don't like either of those plans.'

'Why not, Boss? ' asked Stanley who, secretly, was rather taken with the idea of running away. (Especially to Zanzibar).

★★★★★

'Because', said Santa, 'I'm Santa. Giving presents is what I do. If I don't give presents, who am I?'

(And here we find Santa grappling with one of the problems inherent with defining oneself solely, or indeed primarily, through one's work, and in these days of increasing job insecurity we need to ask ourselves is this really a prudent course of action? But I digress. Again. Sorry.)

Stanley looked at his Boss,
whom he loved very much,
and who he could see was
very, very unhappy. He thought
back over all that had
happened in the last few days.

And he realised that now was the defining moment of his life. The moment for which he would be remembered forever. Or the moment which would consign him to oblivion like that group that came seventh in the 1989 Eurovision Song Contest.

Now was the moment when
he had to come up with a big
idea.

So he racked his brain. He thought about everything he had ever seen. He thought about everything he had ever read. He thought about what he believed was good and what he believed was bad. Finally he spoke.

＊★✷

'So what we need', said Stanley, 'are presents that are small, easy to carry, don't cost much, aren't mass-marketed, over-packaged, over-hyped, over-priced, consumer trash and that would ideally demand something of the recipient beyond just mindless consumption.'

'Yes,' said Santa, somewhat taken aback by Stanley's sudden erudition. 'That would be perfect. What did you have in mind?'

✦ ★ ✦

'I've got no idea,' said Stanley.

And there the whole story would have ended had Stanley not done what he always did when he was stuck for an idea.

He went to his bookshelf for
inspiration.

And found it.

'Books!' cried Stanley 'What about books! Why don't we get people to give each other books!'

'Books?' said Santa in an 'I'm not at all sure, but by your excessive enthusiasm I can see you're really taken with the idea, so let's run it up the flag pole and see who salutes it' kind of a voice.

'Yeah,' said Stanley. ' Books are brilliant. They're full of everything. Everything that ever existed. And everything that anyone could ever imagine existing. Like dinosaurs. And dragons. And games. And horses. And goodies. And baddies. And cheese. And magic. And how to look after pets. And the history of the flugelhorn. And footballers. And how to use an egg coddler. And other countries. And other worlds. And ideas. And the difference between satsumas and clementines. And happy endings. And tax dodges. And everything.'

‘And books aren't heavy?’
asked Santa.

'No' said Stanley, 'they aren't.
Well paperbacks aren't. And
they don't need much
wrapping paper either.'

'Hmmmmmmm,' said Santa.
(Well he didn't actually say it,
he hmmmed it).

'Or Book Tokens,' said Stanley.
'Book Tokens are very light.
And then people can choose
the books they want.'

'Stanley,' said Santa, 'you are a genius. That is a great plan.'

But then Stanley's face fell.
'But how do we tell people?'
he said. And that's when Santa
had his great idea.

'We'll write a book, Stanley. We'll tell people everything you've discovered. And all about Festivco plc. We'll tell them your plan. And people will be able to give the book to each other because we'll make sure it doesn't cost much. And we'll name the book after you,' said Santa.

There was a pause. Then
Stanley spoke.

'But do you really think
Stanley's a good name for a
book?' he said, a little obtusely.

It was shortly after this that Stanley approached me and told me the whole story and asked me to help him get the book written and published.

That's when I explained to him
what Santa had meant about
the book's title.

And when Stanley realised his mistake, I have to admit, he blushed.